Pran's Week of Adventure

written by Tina Athaide

illustrated by Lisa Cinelli

Bebop Books

An imprint of LEE & LOW BOOKS Inc.

On Sunday Mrs. Patel's car broke down.
The car had to go to the shop to be fixed.

Mrs. Patel had to find another way
to take Pran to school.

On Monday Mrs. Patel and Pran took the bus.

The ride was fun but they got on the wrong bus.
They ended up at the beach.

On Tuesday Mrs. Patel and Pran took the train.

The ride was quiet and they fell asleep.
They missed their stop.

On Wednesday Mrs. Patel and Pran took the ferry.

The ride was bumpy and they felt sick.
They went back home to rest.

On Thursday Mrs. Patel and Pran took a taxi.

The ride was fast but the taxi broke down.
They had to take another taxi.

On Friday Mrs. Patel and Pran rode their bikes.

The ride was fun but Pran's bike got a flat tire.
They walked the rest of the way.

On Saturday Mrs. Patel and Pran went to the shop

The shop was busy but the car was ready.
They drove home without any trouble!